Women and Relapse

About the pamphlet
The author describes how the causes for relapse among recovering women are often a function of their social roles and the attitudes of others. Drawing on her counseling experiences and case histories, Ms. Cusack details women's problems in recovery and suggests ways to help avoid relapses.

About the author
Suzanne Boylston Cusack is a New York State credentialed alcoholism and substance abuse counselor (CASAC). Ms. Cusack developed the Women's Program at Veritas Villa, a rehabilitation center she cofounded with her husband, Jim, in 1973. Veritas Villa is located in Kerhonkson, New York.

Hazelden Classics for Continuing Care

Women and Relapse

Revised Edition

Suzanne Boylston Cusack, CASAC, NCACII

Hazelden
Center City, Minnesota 55012-0176

1-800-328-9000
1-651-213-4590 (Fax)
www.hazelden.org

ISBN: 978-0-89486-237-3

Any stories or case studies that may be used in this material are composites of many individuals. Names and details have been changed to protect identities.

Cover and interior design by David Spohn
Typesetting by Tursso Companies

Dedication

Thank God for the gift of sobriety. For my family, friends, and loved ones who touched my life and taught me so much. Special thanks to my husband, best friend, and partner in life, Jim.

INTRODUCTION

What happens when a chemically dependent woman, sober for one week, one month, one year, or twenty years, has a relapse? Does the amount of time make it any better or worse? Are circumstances leading to relapse different for men and women? Are the effects of a relapse worse for women than for men? What about significant others? What are their reactions when a woman who has been sober, drinks or takes other drugs again? Are there metabolic differences between relapsing men and women?

These and so many more questions need to be answered, and I will in no way claim to have all the answers. What I hope to do is explore these questions and other issues, share my findings from actual case histories, and raise new questions, new interest, and research topics in a subject that is still new territory—female addiction.

SELF-ESTEEM

There is initially one common thread connecting chemically dependent women in treatment—guilt and shame over addiction in general, and specifically over their "unladylike" actions while drinking or using other drugs. Most women find it easy to voice the fact that chemical addiction is an illness but have a very difficult time truly believing it in their hearts and minds. No matter what the American Medical Association says or what the best treatment center or counselor tells them, they feel deep inside that it was not "ladylike" to have acted and lived as they did.

Recovery is not easy for the young woman who was the victim of incest at age fourteen, gave up a child for adoption at age sixteen, and supported herself as a prostitute until age twenty-one. How does she convince herself in a few weeks, or even months, that she was "just sick," and all is forgiven now? How does she raise her self-esteem and begin to command respect from the opposite sex? How does the recovering woman, married thirty years, accept the fact that her drinking husband may be sicker than she, and that his sickness as well as her own causes him to "set her up" to drink? When she tries to stay sober, what will he do? When she relapses, how much more difficult is it for her to find any hope?

Even if and when a woman manages to accept and deal with her addiction and forgive herself, she often runs into the problem of her family's lack of acceptance. Family members are ready to let her assume the guilt and remind her of her unacceptable behavior. Her family has a difficult time seeing her as a sick person with an addiction, a person who can change and get well. I find this far more true with the female of any age than with the male. Men usually find that once they show remorse, their parents, spouses, girlfriends, boyfriends, or children forgive them.

Taking all this into consideration for initial treatment, one can easily see why a woman being treated for a second, third, or multiple relapse would have overwhelming problems with recovery. If her own attitudes and self-esteem were affected so deeply the first time around, how much more serious the second, and so on? How many more defense mechanisms must she have to protect that fragile self underneath? How "tough" or overly dependent must she be to face and deal with the few significant others who are left in her life? How much damage was done metabolically? Might she not even be reachable or teachable for a few months?

The more relapses a woman suffers, the less support she receives. Most of the twenty-six to thirty-year-old women who come to me with a history of three to five relapses have very little family involvement in their recovery. Children are usually with the ex-husband or parents. Parents have given up. No one wants these patients, and they are prime candidates for "male dependency addiction," which perpetuates their sickness and low self-esteem. Once a woman begins the relapse syndrome, regardless of her age, it appears she has very little hope of recovering unless she can be given the opportunity of a great deal of time in a controlled environment and with an extremely solid support system for aftercare.

Let us look at why relapse can be more dangerous to women than men. Alcohol generally has a more debilitating effect on women than men simply because of the female's hormonal makeup and general metabolism. Women and men differ in relative amounts of body fat and water. Women have a higher proportion of fat and a lower amount of water, and alcohol is *not* fat-soluble. So a woman and man drinking the same amount of alcohol will have different blood alcohol levels. Hers will be higher because she has less water in which to dilute the alcohol.

Alcoholics generally retain more alcohol than nonalcoholics, and females retain it for longer periods of time than males. While the alcohol is in her system, the blood is constantly carrying it to her vital organs, where it is metabolized more slowly than in a man's body. Consider the women who have relapsed at least two and three times. Is it any wonder why, at age thirty, physical damage could be equated to that of a man ten years or more her senior?

Additional time is needed for a woman's body to recover from the effects of drugs and clean itself out. Research on metabolic differences by gender, and their effects on mental and physical recovery rates, shows that women generally need more initial recovery time to avoid relapse. After a first relapse, women will also need more emotional support, physical allowances, and much more time to recover than they have been given in the past. Perhaps through lack of knowledge, we have been treating women in relapse with the same approach we use with men. But research is showing that we are treating two completely separate pieces of "machinery." We don't know enough yet about metabolism, relapse, or addiction in general, but what we learn through new studies will allow us to develop more effective methods for treating dependent women and thus help them avoid relapse.

Now that we have noted some actual metabolic differences and determined the need to reexamine our treatment of women in relapse, let us go a step further and discuss another common thread running through almost every story—lack of support systems.

SUPPORT SYSTEMS

One of the most significant and prevalent differences in women who relapse, as compared to men, is their lack of support from family members or significant others. In my experience working with relapsing females, I have rarely found a case where this is not true. Even in those cases where an apparent support system exists, it frequently exists for appearances only.

By comparison, it is not as difficult for a relapsing male to retain his support system. He may receive counseling through an employee assistance program, for example. He may also find it easier to gain support from his partner or significant other than a woman would gain from others. Parents are often more willing to overlook what their son has done in the past, seeing his escapades as part of a male growing-up phase. In contrast, while mothers are frequently the most supportive of a relapsing daughter, they find it difficult to accept inappropriate behavior caused by drug use.

This difference in attitudes toward relapsing males and females is also evident when they begin to recover. The male will often enter rehabilitation with his parent's full support, even after many relapses. His sisters and brothers will also appear for counseling and will support him. But a woman's relatives are often angry, not willing to forgive, and blame her for the hurt they feel. While children of either a relapsing male or female feel angry and frustrated, they will usually visit a male relative right away. But I can cite many cases where daughters refuse to visit or even acknowledge a mother who has relapsed just once or twice. In one case, three sons acted as if their mother had died and was no longer a member of their family. They had discovered that she was sexually involved with her husband's best friend and were unwilling to forgive her. It's fairly common for men to be forgiven similar behavior and given many chances to change. In many cases, these attitudes are determined by social expectations that have been in place for generations. Society expects women to fulfill a role that precludes drunkenness or unacceptable drug-induced conduct. The fact that female dependency has been far less visible in the past has reinforced these social expectations and hindered understanding of women's problems with alcohol or other drug dependency.

This lack of understanding is evidenced in the difficulty of getting a female's family involved in her recovery program. They tend to withdraw rather than face the pain, rejection, and disappointment again. Counselors often have to call and insist, in most cases, that a parent, spouse, or child visit and get involved in family counseling.

Considering the double standard and lack of support, what can a woman expect when she goes home from treatment after a relapse? Let's first look at some problems according to age groups:

An adolescent woman fourteen to nineteen often faces angry, fearful parents who may drink alcohol and use other drugs themselves. Or she may be back in a single-parent home in which there may be little or no supervision. She may also return to her peer group, most of whom are into drugs and sex and have little to look forward to.

A twenty-five- to forty-year old may return home to a jealous husband who will resent her going out to meetings where she may meet other men. He may claim, "At least when she drank or used cocaine, she stayed home." If she has young children, she will have to maintain the household, perhaps hold a job outside the home in order to help pay bills, cook and clean, and somehow find time for meetings and herself.

A forty- to sixty-year old can be single, married, widowed, divorced, sometimes sharing a home with either a male or a female. Women often try, out of guilt, to "make up" for lost time and often overdo it at home, thus setting themselves up for further relapse.

Women are often juggling careers, husbands, and children. They are subject to many unadmitted guilt feelings because they don't fulfill all that the books and articles say they should. Many in this group used to be known as the classic drinking housewife who was going through the "empty nest syndrome." This simply meant that all the children were raised and left the nest, leaving Mom at home alone, bored, depressed, and drinking.

Today I see less of this, but more of a phenomenon I call the "not so empty nest syndrome." In this case, the wife has managed a career and raised a family while drinking, and now is divorced. Problem children, now grown, are moving back home, perhaps playing on her guilt from the past, and often expecting financial support as well. They often bring with them their own children and expect her to be a babysitter. She is afraid to say no and becomes manipulated by her guilt. In many cases, this predicament has led to relapse. It is further complicated by the children pulling away once more or taking over the home and leaving their mother in rehabilitation, using her as the scapegoat. Unless this group deals with the situation in family counseling, the female has little hope of recovery and often encounters recurrent relapses. This is an example of an apparent support system that in reality doesn't exist. On the contrary, it is a deterrent and a direct impediment to her sobriety. It is a classic case of the female allowing herself to be used and abused emotionally by her own family.

Care of the aging parent is another part of the "not so empty nest syndrome"—the addition of aging, and sometimes ill, parents of the woman over forty. This compounds and complicates the situation for the female in recovery. If she doesn't ask for and get help, it might cause pressures, guilt, and resentments that could precipitate a relapse. Caring for an aging parent in the home may provide the outward appearance of an additional support system. On the other hand, the aging parent may be bedridden, a drinking alcoholic, and a burdensome addition to a woman's responsibilities for older children and other daily issues. Some of these extended family situations are helpful but many are detrimental. If these situations exist, they should be dealt with to prevent them from standing in the way of full recovery. It should also be pointed out to the patient how she herself may be reluctant to address and change the situation as she may be using it as her excuse to drink.

The sixty-plus "baby boomer" female is often characterized by "delayed drinking" or early senility. Delayed onset drinkers may not have started drinking until they were forty or fifty, and they experience strong denial because they did enjoy years of controlled drinking. When they return home too soon, they have little to stimulate them. If they live in housing for the elderly, their children often leave them there to fend for themselves. Drinking in these situations is sometimes an accepted way of life and anyone living in that environment is a prime candidate for relapse.

If a woman in this age group has relapsed often, her metabolism is less able to recover quickly. So we may encounter bouts of early senility where it may take two or three months for her to make any progress, and she may do so with a limited scope of reality. No one can predict the outcome, as each case is different. We ask the family for time and do everything possible to keep the patient in treatment, as she is often not rational and will insist on leaving prematurely.

Most relapses in this age group occur because

1. There is a lack of family involvement. Husbands are usually absent due to death or divorce; children have often written her off as hopeless.

2. She returns too soon to her previous environment, lacking a support system, and is still in complete denial, incapable of seeing anything else but loneliness and the comfort of the next drink. She often feels there is no hope or reason to live, and the metabolic damage has often left her organs severely affected, particularly her liver and brain.

3. If there still is a family, often funds are limited for rehabilitation, and the family expects her to recover in a short time. Many think this will help her see the folly of her ways, and they then attempt to move her in with them. This is usually a mistake as it can be another apparent support system riddled with resentment and sickness. She will need AA involvement and a new outlook on life. She often becomes a babysitter and feels a prisoner in her child's home, leading to another relapse. Returning this woman to her own home or apartment without a support system is just as disastrous.

Sufficient time for recovery and alternate support systems must be planned for in rehabilitation. Unfortunately, our society provides few live-in support situations for any females, much less the elderly alcoholic. In our program at Veritas Villa, we have a unique setup that blends our elderly patients in with our current rehabilitation and family program. It gets them involved with young and old in many daily activities, much like the extended family of long ago. Our retired elderly women who stay three months feel needed and wanted and often become surrogate parents or grandparents for many of our patients. Each one has her own treasured job. This part of our program evolved naturally and comfortably, and we hope to expand on it, especially as our baby boomer generation continues to mature.

We believe many relapses could be prevented if both women and their families recognize that they will need ample time in treatment. Patience is needed. How much time? We don't want to be held to a definite amount, but certainly a minimum of four to five weeks. Beyond that it should be determined by the individual, her counselor, and the extenuating circumstances.

Naturally, in all these age groups, some women have managed to stay sober regardless of the difficulties they faced. They are women who came to a spiritual awakening within themselves, realized that chemicals were their problem, and desired sobriety above all else. However, many women have died after recurring relapses. It is these women we hope to reach before they die of cirrhosis, heart disease, and other effects of chemical dependency.

Now let's explore a few specific examples, taken at random from my case history files, to describe my experience with female relapse in various age groups. These cases will illustrate the lack of support for the female. The names have been changed, of course. They are only a few cases of people from various walks of life, but they are a good representation of most of my female case histories of relapse.

Adolescents

Rita was sixteen when she came to our treatment center. She had been using marijuana and alcohol since age twelve. She had been raised by her mentally ill and alcoholic mother and had been raped by a stepfather at age eleven. Rita's denial made it obvious that she didn't want to stop using drugs. We kept Rita for about six weeks and within a short time she responded to the love and care; it was probably the first supportive homelike care she had ever received. She hated to leave and that's always a bad sign. We attempted to work with the mother and did persuade her to go for some psychiatric/alcoholic counseling. We also attempted to locate a stable family member to care for Rita. There were none and the mother insisted she return with her. Rita inevitably relapsed. There were no support systems, no change in environment, a direct return to her chemically addicted peer group, and no hope from her point of view. Up to that time, Rita had been truly trying and even enjoying her sober, solid life. Eventually, she joined the Navy (found her own support system and surrogate family), stayed sober, and married. Today we know more and can offer more to young female adolescents in the way of long-term treatment. Many young females have relapsed because of un-cooperative parents and lack of adolescent treatment facilities.

And now let's look at some positive reentry cases following rehabilitation where a constructive support system actually existed and was cooperative, where rehabilitation or aftercare created a surrogate family support system, or a combination of both occurred. Of course, each is an individual case and must be treated as such.

Betty was seventeen when her parents brought her in for treatment, fighting, cursing, and kicking. All she wanted was to leave and see her fiancé, who was also an addict. After much confrontation, Betty agreed to stay. She stayed for four months, and we became her surrogate support family. She learned to relate to the other young women, developed self-esteem, and, with the help of her new female peer group, chose to break off the detrimental engagement. After many difficult family sessions, the parents reluctantly agreed to go for family counseling. As in the case of so many young female clients, the parents often avoided discussing their own marriage problems by focusing on their addicted child. Once the child is in treatment and remains there long enough, parents can seldom avoid their own problems. The parents and child all healed, both separately and together in frequent sessions. Betty returned home to a healthier, more loving, and supportive home and did not relapse.

Young Adult Women

Peggy was a twenty-two-year-old cross-addicted female referred to us by her parish priest. The priest warned us, "There are a lot of deep, serious problems there, more than alcohol," and Peggy arrived labeled as schizophrenic. She was an only child, raised in an apparently "perfect" home. She was lavished with material things and until age sixteen was considered the perfect child. Then she began using alcohol and marijuana, and her personality rapidly changed. After a nervous breakdown at seventeen, her parents rushed her off to a psychiatric ward where she was given Thorazine and various other medications and labeled a paranoid schizophrenic. This led her to pill addiction and to believe she was mentally ill. Because she was chemically dependent, every time she was withdrawn from medication she reacted terribly, so she was given heavier doses. No one suspected chemical addiction as the main problem until, at age twenty-one, she was referred to us. After a thorough detoxification, psychiatric evaluation, and six weeks of inpatient rehabilitation, we are happy to report Peggy is doing well with her new temporary surrogate family at an all-women's halfway house. Simultaneously, her parents are in family treatment and recovering at home.

Sally was twenty-eight years old when she came in for treatment. She had been dating a married man for seven years and was "addicted" to him as well as to alcohol and Valium. Try as she would, she could not picture life without either substance, and she had tried to quit all by herself. She arrived full of guilt and felt she was a very bad person. She knew nothing about AA or the experiences of other women in treatment. There had been a history of alcoholism in her family for years but it wasn't identified as such. She was the first female in her family to admit being alcoholic. Her mother and brother got involved in her treatment and stood by her while the rest of the family continued to drink. Little was known then about women and alcoholism or Valium addiction. She got through it with the support of the staff and her mother, who went to meetings with her. After six weeks in treatment, Sally went home for a visit, and wanted a drink or pill badly, but remembered what she had been told: "If you can't handle it, if it's too soon, come back." She felt guilty about it, thought she might be a lot sicker than she was, and had to face more criticism from still-drinking family members. But she came back into treatment, completed four more months of rehabilitation and got help for her withdrawal from the relationship and the chemicals. When she did return home, her family had a better understanding and was more able to be supportive as she slowly worked her way back into society. Without the extra support, and family help, she probably would have relapsed.

Sister Danielle had been a nun for eighteen years when, at age thirty-five, she was brought to us with a pill addiction. Danielle was the first nun in her community being treated for addiction. She was very angry, guilty, and ashamed, but admitted things had been going wrong with her life and was relieved to do something about it. Her mother superior was very supportive and understanding and in complete agreement with the treatment plan and length of time it required.

Sister Danielle's biggest hurdle was her low self-esteem and inability to accept her addiction as an illness. Her severe anger at herself and her situation was almost always turned inward. She suffered deep depressions and withdrew from her group, requesting almost daily counseling. She constantly wanted to leave and felt she would never get better. She always wanted her counselors to give her an estimate: "When will I get well?" She refused to permit us any contact with her family and insisted they would never understand and forgive.

In due time, she did give permission, and a visit was arranged with her brother and his wife, which went well. She felt they loved and accepted her and her illness, and her self-esteem rose. But when her sister visited a week later, that did not go as well. Her sister was angry and uncooperative. It turned out she was married to a drinking alcoholic and found it difficult to accept this "business of it being a sickness." She accused Danielle of escaping her responsibilities; after all, she was raising a family, working to keep finances going, and was denying the consequences of her husband's drinking. She was the typical enabler and martyr and no one was helping her. She felt Danielle had it easy and left angry and unimpressed. Initially, this shattered Danielle.

Many months later, with the full emotional support of her religious community, Danielle and her counselor visited with her mother. It was the first time Danielle was able to see and accept her mother for what she was, not what Danielle wanted her to be. The counselor observed the interaction and afterward was able to point out the mother was a typical mother, with her own limitations, and that was okay. Danielle was able to understand her mother's pain and frustration in life and so was able to forgive and begin healing, as well as start a new relationship with her.

In the meantime, the religious community had been working too, led by a very kind and forward-thinking mother superior. She had addressed the entire community in meetings and newsletters about addiction, saying it should no longer be hidden by other sisters. The mother superior had also invited a very well-known doctor to lecture at a mandatory general meeting for the sisters.

Danielle was recovering quite well, and her self-esteem and acceptance were so high that she volunteered to write a self-disclosing letter to her community for her first anniversary to thank them openly for their support. She was a pioneer and recognized that her community of sisters believed in her and loved her, even when she had not believed in herself. She was well enough now to be grateful. The letter was not only well received, but was the reason three more sisters went for help.

We think this story of a small community of religious women banding together in support and love for another sister is an example of what is needed if women are to fully recover and avoid relapse. All but one of approximately twelve nuns who have come to us for treatment are still sober—even those who had relapsed before. We attribute this to the time given for rehabilitation, but we would never have been given the time if their communities had not supported them physically, emotionally, and spiritually. Religious communities of nuns are growing more supportive of their chemically addicted sisters and getting them well. They have a built-in fellowship based on mutual love and support. Women's halfway houses and all-women's groups are doing the same for lay women. Women helping women in recovery have unbeatable strength and power in the recovery process. But women are teaching each other how to recover from an illness where treatment often is directed by men and still carries with it a tremendous stigma for the female. We can and must change this stigma, and we believe we can do it only as women helping women, as in the strength of the religious community.

Mature Adult Women

Daisy was a fifty-two-year-old wife of a city employee, referred to us for treatment after a recurrent history of detoxification, AA, and relapse. Daisy lived with her husband, Tom, who didn't drink. Tom visited the rehabilitation center every weekend and was apparently quite devoted to her. Tom had never gone to Al-Anon and had never sought any help for himself. Finally, his employer noticed problems with his work performance, knew he did not drink, but discovered most of his tardiness and absences were due to his wife's binges. In counseling Daisy and Tom, we discovered a severe case of enabling. Over the past ten years Tom had geared his life and activities around Daisy. The children saw what was happening, but neither parent would admit to the problem, and finally the children gave up in disgust and moved away. As Daisy's binges worsened, Tom adapted his coping methods. At first he would miss work only on Mondays to clean house and get Daisy "squared away," but as the years progressed her binges became more frequent and more violent. In an effort to protect himself, he admitted keeping a straightjacket in his closet to restrain Daisy during her episodic explosions. He admitted to living like this for years and was relieved to get help.

Daisy endured years of denial, protection, and enabling because she was a female. Her recurrent relapses were due to only partial family treatment and her return to the same unhealthy environment where no changes occurred. Finally, Daisy was kept in treatment for a few months, and her husband admitted his problem and accepted help. Both recovered together.

Virginia was about fifty-two, a registered nurse, and the wife of a prominent employee assistance program counselor and recovering alcoholic. Compared to her husband Kevin's drinking prior to his entry into AA, her drinking was what she and her husband considered "social." Over the years, Kevin got sober in AA, became very active and successful, and eventually helped develop an employee assistance program. Virginia's drinking progressed along with her pill-taking, which she claimed was medicine needed for her menopause. She became a typical closet drinker and Kevin continually looked the other way, cajoled, nagged, promised her rewards, excused, and did all the usual enabling, while denying his wife's problem. Her husband finally admitted drinking might be her problem. Kevin put her in detoxification and tried to take her to AA, but she refused to go to meetings. It wasn't long before Virginia drank again, but Kevin was pleased she was sober for three months and was hopeful she could control it. Even though he was in AA himself and an alcoholism counselor, he did not want to recognize her problem. After continued relapses, Kevin talked Virginia into going to treatment for one week. But neither he nor her family would truly confront her and insist she stay longer.

Virginia is living in a very disguised support system. She sobers up; runs to AA; avoids involvement with other women; and looks to Kevin for protection, counseling, and enabling. Because Kevin has helped so many others, he finds it difficult to accept that his own family is crumbling. Friends can't reach them, and Virginia's disease progresses. She is living in an unhealthy environment where no changes occur.

Monica was about fifty-six and had been drinking for around thirty-five years. George, her husband of thirty years, is a lawyer, and they have three daughters. George tried treating Monica himself for many years and succeeded in becoming her enabler. There were also many sexual problems that became evident over the years, and one problem heightened the other. Finally, in desperation, George gave up and brought Monica to treatment. This was the first of many inpatient stays that lasted as long as four months at a time. In checking discharge summaries from Monica's previous treatments, there is one glaring problem: she left against counselor and facility advice; her husband insisted and enabled her to leave. Did the husband really want his wife to recover? Every time she reached a plateau of recovery and self-knowledge, George began day-visiting, followed by overnight visits, followed by a request to take her home. His reasons were all valid and within his rights as a husband, but frustrating to the treatment center. Prior to her last admission, I made him agree to allow her an uninterrupted six-month period. A recent psychiatric evaluation determined Monica will do well in a controlled environment only. This, too, is a mutually unhealthy relationship that can only be controlled by separation and separate treatment for both. Every time Monica has returned home she has had a relapse, and each time it has taken its toll on her mental capabilities.

LOOKING AHEAD

Few research findings about relapse and/or female relapse have been compiled to date. One of my hopes is that women will read this booklet, identify, and ask for the help they need to *prevent* relapse. Another hope is that counselors and treatment staff will read it, comment, and learn to identify and help other women with problems similar to those I've described. My ultimate hope is that recovering women, women who treat women, and women in general will read, share, and begin to create more of the nurturing and effective treatment and survival network for recovering females everywhere.

Based on my 1,500 case histories, I believe that where there is an accepting support system, women recover and relapse is prevented. Almost all female relapses occur where there is a weak, detrimental, or absent support system. Perhaps one of the most detrimental "support systems" that can occur is also the most deplored violation in any code of ethics—exploitation of a patient by a professional. This exploitation, emotional, sexual, or otherwise, constitutes betrayal at its worst for the client. The professional who is guilty of the exploitation is often the very last person the patient has decided to trust. Once she realizes she has been taken advantage of, she may never trust again. To make matters worse, if she reveals the violation to others, she may not be taken seriously, perhaps not even believed. She is often made to appear the seducer whereas the professional male involved is often never even questioned or confronted. Unfortunately, there are some professionals who engage in unethical practices, and women should be cautioned to engage only those highly recommended by reputable counseling centers.

RESISTANCE ON THE HOME FRONT

Another glaring difference we have noted between recovering men and women, and one that may be a contributing factor to female relapse, is the less supportive home reentry environment. Statistics indicate that nine out of ten women remain with an alcoholic husband who drinks. From my experience, most women are completely willing to change their lifestyles in any way to accommodate and help the spouse not to drink—unless she herself has a drinking problem. Wives will attend all meetings required, remove liquor from the home, opt not to drink at all if needed, forego drinking affairs and friends, and rearrange family plans. On the other hand, statistics show only one of out ten husbands remains with a drinking wife by the time she appears for treatment.

The classic example is that of the surgeon who remained married to his wife, a registered nurse, for thirty-five years of her binge drinking and never did anything to get help for her. When she finally did seek help on her own, he went through the motions of family counseling but quit the day he was told that he, too, was ill. The wife was recovering, but he couldn't handle it. It threatened his image. Counselors could see the doctor was angry, insecure, and fearful, but was able to hide behind the facade of the long-suffering husband.

In her first year of sobriety he continually attacked her efforts at sobriety and managed to manipulate the children against her. He refused to stop his before-dinner drinking and even convinced her she should make drinks for him, which she did with difficulty. He refused to attend any meetings with her, resented her new friends, and insisted he was not about to change his lifestyle. After two years of this she was headed for a relapse out of sheer frustration. She came to rehabilitation for two weeks, continued outpatient counseling near her home, and finally had to separate for a time in hopes of forcing him to be introspective. He is now going to private counseling.

Most women feel very guilty already, have been told how lucky they are their husbands are still there in view of statistics, and are really afraid to rock the boat. In family counseling they will never dream of raising these issues of changing lifestyles unless it is stressed by the counselor. The wife may accept peace at any price, which may well lead to another relapse. If these issues are confronted, it can make a difference. Even if the husband refuses to change, at least she can be reassured she is not all wrong in her wishes or needs but can choose what is comfortable for her. She can still live soberly in the situation but will have to accept the need to gather strength and support from other areas.

Let's take a look at another example of a recovering female and her husband. While he was glad she stopped drinking, he made it quite clear she should do whatever was necessary to remain abstinent as long as it did not change his life in any way. He continued with his before-dinner cocktails, and she was still expected to attend frequent cocktail parties that were part of the socializing necessary to his business. Whenever they went on business trips or vacations, drinking was also a part of the ordeal. He thought there was nothing wrong with purchasing a pint bottle of gin, or asking her to purchase a bottle while he was at a meeting, so he could still have his cocktail before dinner. Her early-sobriety alcohol cravings, discomfort, and tension grew into full-blown resentment and anger toward her husband, the more powerful because they were unexpressed. Perhaps if she had made him aware of her feelings, things would have been different, but many husbands expect their wives to adapt to them, not the reverse.

How many women, even with all the family counseling available, feel so guilty about their past drinking that they remain married to an "unchanged spouse"? How many of these women truly try to stay sober and have the best intentions but can't handle their untreated spouse? Their loyalty or fear of being left alone frightens them and sends more females back into relapse.

RELAPSE AND HORMONES

One little-explored area concerning women and relapse is the possible link between relapse and hormonal flux in the body. Are women especially prone to relapse during, or just before, their menstrual periods? Is relapse more likely during menopause? Irritability, depression, and other emotional difficulties may be common at these times, and women may find themselves more vulnerable to relapse.

Indeed, some researchers have studied menstruation and menopause in connection to female criminal episodes. Why wouldn't it be just as important to study these in connection to the relapse phenomenon? All agree that certain metabolic changes do occur that cause changes in body fluids, hormones, the brain, and thinking patterns. If a survey could be conducted by knowledgeable gynecologists, one wonders what would be discovered in the area of *prevention* of relapse.

On the other hand, we must also be careful not to go overboard. If a young woman new to treatment has abdominal cramps, the pain might be related to menstruation, to her withdrawal symptoms—or to something else entirely. Many of these young girls (and older women) often do have other medical problems that may be masked by menstruation or menopause. Obviously, awareness of both sides of the issue is the key to finding the answers. If we look at each person as an individual, a new life puzzle to sort out and help piece together, we may be more helpful than ever before.

I am not attempting to make excuses for relapses; all addicted people are experts at that. I am attempting to share case histories, research findings, and comparisons to present some common symptoms in female addiction and relapse, just as doctors compare notes and findings on any other illness.

EMOTIONAL INVOLVEMENT

Women often need help in withdrawing from a third addiction—male dependency. Many women in their progression into chemical addiction have been exploited and thus are very disillusioned with men. As a result they have been deeply hurt, and if these and similar feelings are continued in sobriety, relapse is likely to follow.

Perhaps the most serious barrier to male or female recovery at any age is emotional involvement too soon in their sobriety. It is generally recommended that new members in Alcoholics Anonymous avoid romantic involvements for at least one year and we at Veritas Villa promote this also, as a bare minimum. Most young women need so desperately to discover who they are, learn to make true female friends and trust other women, and thereby establish their own self-esteem before they are ready to bring love to a relationship or select a healthy relationship.

To help prevent these premature involvements, I have had the most success by separating men and women going through treatment and forbidding any form of communication between them. It works. It saves lives, and if we really believe addiction is an illness, then we must begin to look at the cause and effect of the "love addiction" in relation to female relapse. It is a prime cause and we can do something about its prevention.

Some women have very sincerely gone to AA with hopes of continued sobriety while still in very vulnerable emotional states. Some drank only at home and now find themselves exposed to more problems attending meetings than they ever did at home. In general, members in AA are discouraged from sponsoring people of the opposite sex, especially if the new member or sponsee is newly sober. Men and women may have intimate issues, especially when new in recovery, that are best addressed in the confidentiality between same-sex members. But I have seen, time and time again, vulnerable young women preyed upon by male group members. This has led to relapse for both men and women, but it can be far more devastating to the female as it may be the last time her spouse or children will forgive her.

What can we do? Encourage the formation of more "women only" groups that meet in the evening as well as during the day. In areas where this has been done there have been tremendous results:

- better and stronger fellowship among women
- more responsible and longer term sponsorship
- more shared sponsorship for newcomers
- women monitoring and protecting other women from the "hazards of sobriety" such as early dating
- miraculous results for a few women who were considered "hopeless relapsers"

The few we turned over to these groups have responded beautifully to the daily phone calls, luncheon visits, fun activities, and tender loving care of women caring for women.

Women aren't always capable, especially after being sober for awhile, of reaching out to other women in a new group or new area. Many women have relapses following a move to a new community, even after having a period of good sobriety. It goes back to women fearing and not trusting other women; it takes time for women to make new friends.

Perhaps we who are sober and active in women's groups can be aware of this and in our relapse prevention efforts do a little extra reaching out to newcomers. They may have just moved and arrive at our group looking very organized, perhaps even a little snobbish to cover up their fear and lack of trust. Look beyond the facade, reach out, and don't give up. She is afraid, lonely, and besides, it could be *you* the next time you must relocate. If a woman arrived drunk at your group's door, everyone would be sure to help. Let's not neglect the newcomer who arrives sober, and even more so, let's not neglect or miss the "dry drunk" symptoms we have found to be common to women prior to their relapse:

- isolation and withdrawal
- continued depression and lack of interest
- sloppy appearance
- frequent crying

If we truly believe addiction is an illness, then we must also believe that, as with any illness, relapse is possible. Perhaps we are fortunate because it is an illness in which certain common symptoms often become apparent prior to the actual relapse. We can become more in tune with these symptoms in our support groups and be on guard for each other in a more open, helpful way.

It is already an admitted fact that women are the "hidden alcoholics," capable of disguising their illness for years. I go one step further and state that women, prior to relapse, are far more adept than men at hiding and masking "dry drunk" relapse symptoms. Add to this mix the current nightmare of methamphetamine and prescription drugs and we see more and more women relapsing after many years of sobriety. As in our active drinking days, others will perhaps not even notice symptoms prior to relapse. They want to believe that the woman has overcome the problem and won't drink again. So the enabling process can continue prior to and into relapse.

In view of this, women do need to be more conscious of the fact it may be up to them to spot problems in each other ahead of time. Women must be more responsive to other women and help each other. We need to learn how to be a friend to another person, how to listen, be a buddy, be part of a team. Perhaps then we, as women, will draw from our own natural gifts and grow.

UNRESOLVED PROBLEMS

Research on family systems and roles within the framework of an alcoholic family have helped answer and resolve much of what was once pushed under the rug. We see more and more adult children of alcoholics who come to us for alcoholic recovery. All women, and particularly women in relapse, appear to have more difficulty than men in resolving hurts from the past over an alcoholic parent.

Let's discuss a relapsing female patient presenting herself for treatment who still carries anger and resentment toward her own mother. In delving into her family history, the patient needs to realize that her mother was most likely addicted to alcohol, although forty years ago it was rarely recognized as such. Before the patient could forgive herself and accept her illness, she had to understand her mother's illness and forgive her first. Many times this healing makes the difference between sobriety and relapse for the female.

Another common cause of a female patient's relapse is fear of uncovering the family skeleton of incest. Her sobriety is undermined by unresolved problems from her past. I have tried to raise the question of incest in almost all my counseling with females because it is more common than was once believed. The stigma attached to alcoholism is difficult enough for some women without the additional stigma attached to incest. Once her guilt is lessened through counseling and she realizes she was also a victim of her father's (or other relative's) illness, she has a chance of getting well.

Where possible, a healing between the patient and her mother should also be encouraged so that the patient can learn to forgive her mother as well. Most victims blame the mother for the denial she protects herself with and for allowing the incest to go on. Statistics tell us as many as ten million girls and women may have suffered incest, whether by a father, uncle, brother, or other relative. Our chances of meeting a good portion of them in treatment centers are very high.

On the reverse side of the coin, and rarely discussed, is the case of the relapsing female who cannot stay sober because she has committed incest with her son. It is sometimes very difficult to uncover, and it may be the cause of more relapses than we know. After all, society is just beginning to open the door on father and daughter incest. All we can do is be aware that mother and son incest does happen and be prepared to help our patients accept and deal with it.

Another time bomb for relapse is the lesbian who cannot accept herself and her way of life. The lesbian is not so by choice. She is born that way—just as she is not alcoholic, blue-eyed, or tall by choice. Most lesbians are comfortable with their lifestyle. I have found those who acknowledge being gay as openly as one would acknowledge being heterosexual, neither ashamed nor overly proud, do well in recovery.

One young woman had refused to be open about her past. She claimed she just didn't like men but refused to acknowledge being lesbian. When she relapsed and returned—and this time she was told she'd better get honest—she admitted the truth. She was afraid people wouldn't like her if they knew. We taught her to be more accepting of herself, continued our own acceptance and care for her, and reassured her that her sexual orientation did not make her less of a person. Now she believes in her self-worth and is still sober.

I believe that many women relapse over the "unmentionables" that are often considered unimportant and glossed over during counseling:

Abortion—How many has the patient had? Has she been physically damaged? Is she worried that "God will punish her" when she wants to have children? Is she from a strict religious background and still carrying a great deal of guilt? Has she grieved properly over the loss of that child, even if aborted by choice, or has society told her that "it was nothing"? What does she really feel?

Miscarriage—Has she accepted the miscarriage or is she angry about it? Has she grieved properly? How did the miscarriage really affect her? Can she have more children or not?

Children given up—Has the patient ever given up a child for adoption? Even if for the best, does she ever discuss the hurt and pain she must always live with?

Children taken away—How many relapsing females have lost children through court orders? I know one in particular who lost her children to her actively drinking husband. Society saw her as an unfit mother but was sympathetic toward him. Does she discuss the hurt and terrible guilt, or has she lost hope completely? I have found that mothers who have children taken away by court order have a very difficult time with recovery.

Disliking motherhood—How many women married just to leave home and found themselves mothers before they knew they had a choice in the matter? Years later they are still not honest about their dislike of being a mother and are afraid or feel bad about admitting it. So they keep relapsing, never get honest, and see no hope for anything. On the other hand, if this patient can admit her true feelings, she may not change or want to change her life immediately, but she can begin to make plans to go to work or school. She can be taught to make some decisions and choices and have new control over her life. She may find herself full of hope and being a better mother than she ever thought possible.

Indeed, unresolved problems can involve some glaring and sensitive subjects that may snag a woman's recovery. To be honest about everyday pain and disillusionment, and to see new avenues for acceptance and growth, are often the remedy for women in frequent relapse.

SUMMARY

Understanding and staying alert to relapse issues for women can help us maintain long-term sobriety and enjoy a long and lasting recovery. This pamphlet has told many stories of women from various age groups and has offered numerous suggestions for strengthening recovery and preventing relapse. Women need to recognize the issues around self-esteem and continue to enhance our own by changing our negative attitudes and encouraging family support. We can correct our lack of support systems by developing them as outlined here. We need to be cautious of too-soon emotional involvement in early recovery; support and encourage women role models, sponsors, and groups; and resolve problems that threaten to create resentments that can undermine our recovery. Each step we take forward into a healthy recovery keeps us away from relapse and allows us to enjoy and celebrate our freedom.

THE TWELVE STEPS OF ALCOHOLICS ANONYMOUS

1. We admitted we were powerless over alcohol—that our lives had become unmanageable.
2. Came to believe that a Power greater than ourselves could restore us to sanity.
3. Made a decision to turn our will and our lives over to the care of God *as we understood Him.*
4. Made a searching and fearless moral inventory of ourselves.
5. Admitted to God, to ourselves, and to another human being the exact nature of our wrongs.
6. Were entirely ready to have God remove all these defects of character.
7. Humbly asked Him to remove our shortcomings.
8. Made a list of all persons we had harmed, and became willing to make amends to them all.
9. Made direct amends to such people wherever possible, except when to do so would injure them or others.
10. Continued to take personal inventory and when we were wrong promptly admitted it.
11. Sought through prayer and meditation to improve our conscious contact with God *as we understood Him,* praying only for knowledge of His will for us and the power to carry that out.
12. Having had a spiritual awakening as the result of these steps, we tried to carry this message to alcoholics, and to practice these principles in all our affairs.

The Twelve Steps of AA are taken from *Alcoholics Anonymous*, 4th ed., published by AA World Services, Inc., New York, N.Y., 59–60.

Hazelden Publishing is a division of the Hazelden Foundation, a not-for-profit organization. Since 1949, Hazelden has been a leader in promoting the dignity and treatment of people afflicted with the disease of chemical dependency.

The mission of the foundation is to improve the quality of life for individuals, families, and communities by providing a national continuum of information, education, and recovery services that are widely accessible; to advance the field through research and training; and to improve our quality and effectiveness through continuous improvement and innovation.

Stemming from that, the mission of this division is to provide quality information and support to people wherever they may be in their personal journey—from education and early intervention, through treatment and recovery, to personal and spiritual growth.

Although our treatment programs do not necessarily use everything Hazelden publishes, our bibliotherapeutic materials support our mission and the Twelve Step philosophy upon which it is based. We encourage your comments and feedback.

The headquarters of the Hazelden Foundation are in Center City, Minnesota. Additional treatment facilities are located in Chicago, Illinois; Newberg, Oregon; New York, New York; Plymouth, Minnesota; and St. Paul, Minnesota. At these sites, we provide a continuum of care for men and women of all ages. Our Plymouth facility is designed specifically for youth and families.

For more information on Hazelden, please call **1-800-257-7800**. Or you may access our World Wide Web site on the Internet at **www.hazelden.org**.